Table Talk

Creating Meaningful Conversation with Family and Friends

by
Karol Ladd

B&H
PUBLISHING
GROUP

Nashville, Tennessee

Table Talk

*P*ull up a chair and join in a hearty discussion around the table. Dinner tables throughout the ages and around the world have been the primary source for delicious meals and meaningful conversations. Unfortunately, in our hustle-bustle society, the dinner hour is many times replaced by a drive-by meal in the car on the way to practices, lessons, or meetings. Families of the new millennium must be deliberate when it comes to sharing times together. This small book was created to inspire and encourage you to plan memorable dinners together with the blessing of stimulating conversation. Whether you are sharing a meal with family or friends, the questions found on the following pages are able to spark an interest and fuel the flame to vibrant and perhaps life-changing discussions.

You will find a variety of thought-provoking questions under each of the four topics which include: "Historical Moments," "Media Marvels," "Biblical Topics" and "Trends, Fads, and Inventions." Each page begins with a question directed toward ages 9 and older, and is followed by a correlating question for ages 8 and under. Be careful not to judge any person for their answers; instead, offer a forum of honesty as you search together for the truth founded on principles in God's Word. Each question includes a biblical reference in order to offer an eternal perspective or initiate a devotional time after the question has been discussed. Consider using *Table Talk* once a week to add pizzazz to the normal family dinner or bring it out at a casual party or gathering of friends. Use this book as a way to deepen relationships, provoke discussion, or introduce a devotional; but most importantly enjoy the topics as a delightful way to spend quality time together!

Contents

Moments in History

sports accomplishments

advancements

communications

civilizations

time periods

Great Events and
Interesting People

Moments in History

1.
Influential People

In your opinion, what one person had the greatest, positive influence in the 20th Century?

What impact did he or she make on society?

Younger Question: Name someone you know who is special and important to you.

What good things do they do to show they care about you?

What are actions we can do to help and encourage others?

I Thessalonians 5:12-15

Now we ask you, brothers, to respect those who work hard among you, who are over you in the Lord and who admonish you. Hold them in the highest regard in love because of their work. Live in peace with each other. And we urge you, brothers, warn those who are idle, encourage the timid, help the weak, be patient with everyone. Make sure that nobody pays back wrong for wrong, but always try to be kind to each other and to everyone else.

1.
Influential People

Personal Notes:

_____

_____

_____

_____

_____

_____

_____

_____

_____

_____

_____

_____

_____

_____

_____

_____

_____

_____

_____

2.
Time Periods

If you could choose another time period in history in which to live, when would it be?

Why would you want to live during that time?

Younger Question: What do you know about people who lived long ago?

How are their lives different than the way we live today?

Psalm 119:89-90

Your word, O LORD, is eternal; it stands firm in the heavens. Your faithfulness continues through all generations; you established the earth, and it endures.

2.
Time Periods

Personal Notes:

_____

_____

_____

_____

_____

_____

_____

_____

_____

_____

_____

_____

_____

_____

_____

_____

_____

_____

_____

3.
Athletics

In your opinion, what was the most amazing athletic accomplishment by an individual athlete in the past 50 years?

Give reasons for your answer.

Younger Question: What type of sports and activities do you like to do? (examples: running, football, climbing, tumbling, etc.)

Why do you like it, and what do you think is the most difficult part about the sport?

Philippians 3:14

I press on toward the goal to win the prize for which God has called me heavenward in Christ Jesus.

3.
Athletics

Personal Notes:

4.
Wars

Of all the wars in history, in which one would you have wanted to serve and for what cause?

What rank or position would you hope to fill?

Younger Question: What is a war? Why do you think people fight battles?

Ephesians 6:10-20

Finally, be strong in the Lord and in his mighty power. Put on the full armor of God so that you can take your stand against the devil's schemes. For our struggle is not against flesh and blood, but against the rulers, against the authorities, against the powers of this dark world and against the spiritual forces of evil in the heavenly realms. Therefore put on the full armor of God, so that when the day of evil comes, you may be able to stand your ground, and after you have done everything, to stand. Stand firm then, with the belt of truth buckled around your waist, with the breastplate of righteousness in place, and with your feet fitted with the readiness that comes from the gospel of peace. In addition to all this, take up the shield of faith, with which you can extinguish all the flaming arrows of the evil one. Take the helmet of salvation and the sword of the Spirit, which is the word of God. And pray in the Spirit on all occasions with all kinds of prayers and requests. With this in mind, be alert and always keep on praying for all the saints. Pray also for me, that whenever I open my mouth, words may be given me so that I will fearlessly make known the mystery of the gospel, for which I am an ambassador in chains. Pray that I may declare it fearlessly, as I should.

4.
Wars

Personal Notes:

_____

_____

_____

_____

_____

_____

_____

_____

_____

_____

_____

_____

_____

_____

_____

_____

_____

_____

Moments in History

5.
Communication

What advancement in communication had the greatest significance in world history (Gutenberg press, telegraph, telephone, Internet, etc.)?

Explain why you chose your answer.

Younger Question: The telephone, mail, newspaper, and computers are each ways we communicate with others. The word "communicate" means "to share thoughts and ideas with other people."

Which one of these items do you think helps us most and why?

Ephesians 4:29

Do not let any unwholesome talk come out of your mouths, but only what is helpful for building others up according to their needs, that it may benefit those who listen.

5.
Communication

Personal Notes:

_____

_____

_____

_____

_____

_____

_____

_____

_____

_____

_____

_____

_____

_____

_____

_____

_____

_____

_____

_____

_____

6.
Civilizations

If Americans could learn anything from the rise and fall of past civilizations, what lesson should they heed?

Younger Question: Do you think we can learn any lessons from people who lived years ago? What do you think we can learn?

Proverbs 3:21-23

My son, preserve sound judgment and discernment, do not let them out of your sight; they will be life for you, an ornament to grace your neck. Then you will go on your way in safety, and your foot will not stumble.

6.
Civilizations

Personal Notes:

_____

_____

_____

_____

_____

_____

_____

_____

_____

_____

_____

_____

_____

_____

_____

_____

_____

_____

_____

_____

7.
Hard Times

What impact did the great Depression (1929) have on American culture?

What insight and wisdom have we gained from this difficult period of time?

Younger Question: Have you ever learned a lesson from a mistake that you made or something difficult that you went through?

Tell what you learned.

James 1:2-5

Consider it pure joy, my brothers, whenever you face trials of many kinds, because you know that the testing of your faith develops perseverance. Perseverance must finish its work so that you may be mature and complete, not lacking anything. If any of you lacks wisdom, he should ask God, who gives generously to all without finding fault, and it will be given to him.

7.
Hard Times

Personal Notes:

_____

_____

_____

_____

_____

_____

_____

_____

_____

_____

_____

_____

_____

_____

_____

_____

_____

_____

_____

_____

_____

8.
Bravery

Throughout history there have been men and women who were remembered and honored for their bravery.

In your opinion, who offered the greatest display of bravery and courage?

What causes some people to be brave, while others are fearful?

Younger Question: What does it mean to be brave?

Can you name anyone that you know or have heard about in a story who showed bravery or courage?

Joshua 1:9

"Have I not commanded you? Be strong and courageous. Do not be terrified; do not be discouraged, for the LORD your God will be with you wherever you go."

8.
Bravery

Personal Notes:

_____

_____

_____

_____

_____

_____

_____

_____

_____

_____

_____

_____

_____

_____

_____

_____

_____

_____

_____

_____

9.
Evil

Which king, queen or ruler in all of history would you label as the most destructive or evil?

What did they do to deserve this label?

Younger Question: Have you ever read any stories which talk about a bad person?

What makes a person do mean or wrong actions?

Galatians 5:19-23

The acts of the sinful nature are obvious: sexual immorality, impurity and debauchery; idolatry and witchcraft; hatred, discord, jealousy, fits of rage, selfish ambition, dissensions, factions and envy; drunkenness, orgies, and the like. I warn you, as I did before, that those who live like this will not inherit the kingdom of God. But the fruit of the Spirit is love, joy, peace, patience, kindness, goodness, faithfulness, gentleness and self-control. Against such things there is no law.

9.
Evil

Personal Notes:

_____

_____

_____

_____

_____

_____

_____

_____

_____

_____

_____

_____

_____

_____

_____

_____

_____

_____

_____

_____

10.
Explorers

Of the world's numerous explorers, which one do you feel made the most significant discovery in history?

Explain.

Younger Question: What do you think an "explorer" does?

Look in the dictionary together for a definition.

If you could go exploring, where would you start?

Genesis 12:1-3

The LORD had said to Abram, "Leave your country, your people and your father's household and go to the land I will show you. "I will make you into a great nation and I will bless you; I will make your name great, and you will be a blessing. I will bless those who bless you, and whoever curses you I will curse; and all peoples on earth will be blessed through you."

10.
Explorers

Personal Notes:

_____

_____

_____

_____

_____

_____

_____

_____

_____

_____

_____

_____

_____

_____

_____

_____

_____

11.
Disasters

In your opinion, what was the worst natural or man-made disaster in world history?

Could the destruction have been prevented?

Younger Question: Sometimes people go through difficult times: a friend moves away, someone dies, or a person loses his or her job. What can we do to help people when they go through a tough time?

Psalm 61

Hear my cry, O God; listen to my prayer. From the ends of the earth I call to you, I call as my heart grows faint; lead me to the rock that is higher than I. For you have been my refuge, a strong tower against the foe. I long to dwell in your tent forever and take refuge in the shelter of your wings. For you have heard my vows, O God; you have given me the heritage of those who fear your name. Increase the days of the king's life, his years for many generations. May he be enthroned in God's presence forever; appoint your love and faithfulness to protect him. Then will I ever sing praise to your name and fulfill my vows day after day.

11.
Disasters

Personal Notes:

_____

_____

_____

_____

_____

_____

_____

_____

_____

_____

_____

_____

_____

_____

_____

_____

_____

_____

_____

12.
Freedom

Why is freedom important to people and to nations?

Should freedom have its limits?

If so, what limits should it have?

Younger Question: Do you think we should have rules to help us live?

What rules do you think are most important?

Matthew 22:37-40

Jesus replied: "'Love the Lord your God with all your heart and with all your soul and with all your mind.' This is the first and greatest commandment. And the second is like it: 'Love your neighbor as yourself.' All the Law and the Prophets hang on these two commandments."

Also look up: Exodus 20:1-17

12.
Freedom

Personal Notes:

_____

_____

_____

_____

_____

_____

_____

_____

_____

_____

_____

_____

_____

_____

_____

_____

_____

_____

_____

_____

Media Marvels

interviews

movies

FAME

music

Celebrities and Accomplishments

Media Marvels

1. Magazines

2. Music

3. Books

4. Television

5. Newspapers

6. Movies

7. Celebrities

8. Fame

9. Interviews

10. Reading

11. Favorite People

12. Famous People

Media Marvels

1.
Magazines

If you were a writer for a popular magazine, what subject would you choose for your feature story?

Who would you interview?

Tell what type of magazine: news, fashion, sports, etc.

Younger Question: If you could write a special story for a magazine, what kind of story would you write?

Would you write about animals, people, God?

How would it end?

Colossians 3:17

And whatever you do, whether in word or deed, do it all in the name of the Lord Jesus, giving thanks to God the Father through him.

1.
Magazines

Personal Notes:

_____

_____

_____

_____

_____

_____

_____

_____

_____

_____

_____

_____

_____

_____

_____

_____

_____

_____

_____

2.
Music

In what way does music influence you?

What type of music do you listen to?

Who is your favorite musician?

Younger Question: What are your favorite songs, and why do you like them?

Can you say the words to one of the songs?

Colossians 3:16

Let the word of Christ dwell in you richly as you teach and admonish one another with all wisdom, and as you sing psalms, hymns and spiritual songs with gratitude in your hearts to God.

2.
Music

Personal Notes:

_____

_____

_____

_____

_____

_____

_____

_____

_____

_____

_____

_____

_____

_____

_____

_____

_____

_____

3.
Books

If you were going on a week long trip, what type of reading materials would you bring along with you?

Name at least three items.

Younger Question: If you were going on a trip, and you could bring three books with you, which ones would you choose?

Why do you like these books?

Colossians 3:1

Since, then, you have been raised with Christ, set your hearts on things above, where Christ is seated at the right hand of God.

3.
Books

Personal Notes:

_____

_____

_____

_____

_____

_____

_____

_____

_____

_____

_____

_____

_____

_____

_____

_____

_____

_____

4.
Television

How much time each day do you spend watching television?

Why do you watch it?

If you could choose only one program to watch per week, what would it be?

Younger Question: Do you like to watch television?

What is your favorite program to watch?

Who is your favorite character to see on TV?

Romans 12:1-2

Therefore, I urge you, brothers, in view of God's mercy, to offer your bodies as living sacrifices, holy and pleasing to God-- this is your spiritual act of worship. Do not conform any longer to the pattern of this world, but be transformed by the renewing of your mind. Then you will be able to test and approve what God's will is-- his good, pleasing and perfect will.

4.
Television

Personal Notes:

_____

_____

_____

_____

_____

_____

_____

_____

_____

_____

_____

_____

_____

_____

_____

_____

_____

_____

Media Marvels

5.
Newspapers

Can you trust everything you read in the newspaper?

How do you know a story is reliable?

How do you recognize a bias (writer's own opinion or inclination) in an article?

Younger Question: What part of the newspaper do you like to look at or read?

Why do you think newspapers are important to the people in a city?

1 Corinthians 2:4-5

My message and my preaching were not with wise and persuasive words, but with a demonstration of the Spirit's power, so that your faith might not rest on men's wisdom, but on God's power.

5.
Newspapers

Personal Notes:

_____

_____

_____

_____

_____

_____

_____

_____

_____

_____

_____

_____

_____

_____

_____

_____

_____

_____

_____

_____

6.
Movies

If you could write and direct a movie, what would it be about?

Who would star in it?

What message would it send to the viewer?

Younger Question: If you could choose one book to make into a movie or video, which one would it be?

Who would play the main characters?

Colossians 4:5-6

Be wise in the way you act toward outsiders; make the most of every opportunity. Let your conversation be always full of grace, seasoned with salt, so that you may know how to answer everyone.

6.
Movies

Personal Notes:

_____

_____

_____

_____

_____

_____

_____

_____

_____

_____

_____

_____

_____

_____

_____

_____

_____

7.
Celebrities

What is the purpose of getting autographs of celebrities?

Do you have any autographs of famous people?

Whose autograph would you like to have?

Younger Question: What is an autograph?

Why do you think people want to get them from famous people?

Do you want anyone's autograph?

Philippians 2:5-11

Your attitude should be the same as that of Christ Jesus: Who, being in very nature God, did not consider equality with God something to be grasped, but made himself nothing, taking the very nature of a servant, being made in human likeness. And being found in appearance as a man, he humbled himself and became obedient to death-- even death on a cross! Therefore God exalted him to the highest place and gave him the name that is above every name, that at the name of Jesus every knee should bow, in heaven and on earth and under the earth, and every tongue confess that Jesus Christ is Lord, to the glory of God the Father.

7.
Celebrities

Personal Notes:

_____

_____

_____

_____

_____

_____

_____

_____

_____

_____

_____

_____

_____

_____

_____

_____

_____

_____

8.
Fame

In what area of life would you want to be famous or well known: sports, television, writing?

How important is it to you to be famous?

Younger Question: What does it mean to be famous?

Would you want to be famous for something?

If so, what?

Mark 10:43-45

Not so with you. Instead, whoever wants to become great among you must be your servant, and whoever wants to be first must be slave of all. For even the Son of Man did not come to be served, but to serve, and to give his life as a ransom for many.

8.
Fame

Personal Notes: _____

_____

_____

_____

_____

_____

_____

_____

_____

_____

_____

_____

_____

_____

_____

_____

_____

_____

_____

_____

9.
Interviews

If a magazine were to do a feature article about your life, what would be the highlights of the article?

Who would the writer need to interview to get the "scoop" on your life?

What pictures would be included in the article?

Younger Question: If someone were going to write a story just about you, what facts should they know about you? (favorite toys, games, friends, vacations, etc.)

Matthew 5:16

In the same way, let your light shine before men, that they may see your good deeds and praise your Father in heaven.

9.
Interviews

Personal Notes:

Media Marvels
10.
Reading

What is the title of the last book you read or are presently reading?

How is it effecting you?

Why are you reading it?

Would you recommend it to others?

Younger Question: What kind of books do you like to read or have read to you?

Why do you like these books?

Colossians 2:8

See to it that no one takes you captive through hollow and deceptive philosophy, which depends on human tradition and the basic principles of this world rather than on Christ.

10.
Reading

Personal Notes:

_____

_____

_____

_____

_____

_____

_____

_____

_____

_____

_____

_____

_____

_____

_____

_____

_____

_____

11.
Favorite People

If you could invite five people (from any time period) to an exclusive dinner party, who would they be and why?

Younger Question: Think of five people you would like to invite to your house for dinner.

They can be famous people or people from books you have read. Who would you invite and why?

1 Corinthians 10:31

So whether you eat or drink or whatever you do, do it all for the glory of God.

11.
Favorite People

Personal Notes:
_____

_____

_____

_____

_____

_____

_____

_____

_____

_____

_____

_____

_____

_____

_____

_____

_____

_____

_____

_____

_____

Media Marvels

12.
Famous People

What makes a person famous or important?

Is it talent or being in the right place at the right time?

Who do you consider as the most famous person of our day and why?

Younger Question: What do you think makes a person important or well-known?

Who do think is famous today, and why are they famous?

Psalm 1

Blessed is the man who does not walk in the counsel of the wicked or stand in the way of sinners or sit in the seat of mockers. But his delight is in the law of the LORD, and on his law he meditates day and night. He is like a tree planted by streams of water, which yields its fruit in season and whose leaf does not wither. Whatever he does prospers. Not so the wicked! They are like chaff that the wind blows away. Therefore the wicked will not stand in the judgment, nor sinners in the assembly of the righteous. For the LORD watches over the way of the righteous, but the way of the wicked will perish.

12.
Famous People

Personal Notes:

Biblical Thoughts and Themes

Faith

JESUS

miracles

Topics about Faith
and the Faithful

Biblical Thoughts and Themes

1. Biblical Faith

2. Faith Today

3. Women of the Bible

4. Miracles

5. Describing God

6. Jesus

7. Blessings

8. Salt and Light

9. Moses

10. Bible Verses

11. Bible Books

12. Talking to Jesus

Biblical Thoughts and Themes
1.
Biblical Faith

Of the characters found in the Bible, who do you think displayed great faith in God and His Word?

Younger Question: What does it mean to have faith?

Can you name someone in the Bible who showed faith?

Hebrews 11:1-3

Now faith is being sure of what we hope for and certain of what we do not see. This is what the ancients were commended for. By faith we understand that the universe was formed at God's command, so that what is seen was not made out of what was visible.

(For more about people of faith, read the rest of Chapter 11)

1.
Biblical Faith

Personal Notes:

_____

_____

_____

_____

_____

_____

_____

_____

_____

_____

_____

_____

_____

_____

_____

_____

_____

_____

_____

_____

_____

_____

2.
Faith Today

In today's world, who do you know (or know about) who demonstrates an outstanding faith in God?

Why did you choose this person?

Younger Question: Can you name someone you know who is living today, who seems to have a strong faith in God?

Why do you think this person has a strong faith?

James 2:14-17

What good is it, my brothers, if a man claims to have faith but has no deeds? Can such faith save him? Suppose a brother or sister is without clothes and daily food. If one of you says to him, "Go, I wish you well; keep warm and well fed," but does nothing about his physical needs, what good is it? In the same way, faith by itself, if it is not accompanied by action, is dead.

(For more about faith, read the entire chapter)

2.
Faith Today

Personal Notes:

_____

_____

_____

_____

_____

_____

_____

_____

_____

_____

_____

_____

_____

_____

_____

_____

_____

_____

_____

Biblical Thoughts and Themes
3.
Women of the Bible

If you could have a conversation with a female character in the Bible, with whom would you speak?

What questions would you ask her?

Younger Question: If you could choose to meet one of the following women from the Bible, who would you choose? (Eve, Esther, Sarah, Ruth or Mary)

What would you say to her?

Proverbs 31:30-31

Charm is deceptive, and beauty is fleeting; but a woman who fears the LORD is to be praised. Give her the reward she has earned, and let her works bring her praise at the city gate.

3.
Women of the Bible

Personal Notes:

_____

_____

_____

_____

_____

_____

_____

_____

_____

_____

_____

_____

_____

_____

_____

_____

_____

Biblical Thoughts and Themes

4.
Miracles

In your opinion, what was the most profound miracle recorded in the Bible?

Why do you think it ranks above the rest?

Younger Question: What is a miracle?

Can you name one from the Bible that you think is special?

Jeremiah 32:17

"Ah, Sovereign LORD, you have made the heavens and the earth by your great power and outstretched arm. Nothing is too hard for you.

4.
Miracles

Personal Notes:

Biblical Thoughts and Themes

5.
Describing God

What words would you use to describe God to someone who had never read the Bible before?

Younger Question: What words would you use to describe God?

Jeremiah 32:18-20

You show love to thousands but bring the punishment for the fathers' sins into the laps of their children after them. O great and powerful God, whose name is the LORD Almighty, great are your purposes and mighty are your deeds. Your eyes are open to all the ways of men; you reward everyone according to his conduct and as his deeds deserve. You performed miraculous signs and wonders in Egypt and have continued them to this day, both in Israel and among all mankind, and have gained the renown that is still yours.

See also: Psalm 135:1-7, Psalm 23, Psalm 84:11, Psalm 61,62,63

5.
Describing God

Personal Notes:

Biblical Thoughts and Themes

6.
Jesus

Why do you think it was necessary for Jesus to die and rise again?

Younger Question: What do you know about Jesus?

Who was He, and what was His purpose here on earth?

II Corinthians 5:17-21

Therefore, if anyone is in Christ, he is a new creation; the old has gone, the new has come! All this is from God, who reconciled us to himself through Christ and gave us the ministry of reconciliation: that God was reconciling the world to himself in Christ, not counting men's sins against them. And he has committed to us the message of reconciliation. We are therefore Christ's ambassadors, as though God were making his appeal through us. We implore you on Christ's behalf: Be reconciled to God. God made him who had no sin to be sin for us, so that in him we might become the righteousness of God.

See also: Isaiah 53, Romans 5, Hebrews 9

6.
Jesus

Personal Notes:

_____

_____

_____

_____

_____

_____

_____

_____

_____

_____

_____

_____

_____

_____

_____

_____

_____

_____

7.
Blessings

If you were to take a moment now to thank God for the ways He has blessed you, what are the top five blessings you would name?

Younger Question: If you were to thank God for five things, what would they be?

1 Thessalonians 5:18

Give thanks in all circumstances, for this is God's will for you in Christ Jesus.

7.
Blessings

Personal Notes:

8.
Salt and Light

Jesus said His followers are "salt" and "light" in this world. In what ways would you say your life represents salt and/or light in this world?

Younger Question: Jesus said His followers are the "light of the world" How can you be a shining light for the Lord?

Matthew 5:13-16

"You are the salt of the earth. But if the salt loses its saltiness, how can it be made salty again? It is no longer good for anything, except to be thrown out and trampled by men. "You are the light of the world. A city on a hill cannot be hidden. Neither do people light a lamp and put it under a bowl. Instead they put it on its stand, and it gives light to everyone in the house. In the same way, let your light shine before men, that they may see your good deeds and praise your Father in heaven.

8.
Salt and Light

Personal Notes: _____

_____

_____

_____

_____

_____

_____

_____

_____

_____

_____

_____

_____

_____

_____

_____

_____

_____

Biblical Thoughts and Themes

9.

Moses

When you think about the Israelites leaving Egypt and going to the promised land under Moses' leadership, what lessons can you apply to your life today?

Younger Question: Do you remember Moses in the Bible?

Can you name some of the special ways God used Moses to help His people leave Egypt?

Exodus 3:10-12

"...So now, go. I am sending you to Pharaoh to bring my people the Israelites out of Egypt." But Moses said to God, "Who am I, that I should go to Pharaoh and bring the Israelites out of Egypt?" And God said, "I will be with you. And this will be the sign to you that it is I who have sent you: When you have brought the people out of Egypt, you will worship God on this mountain."

Read the entire book of Exodus for more about Moses

9.
Moses

Personal Notes:

_____

_____

_____

_____

_____

_____

_____

_____

_____

_____

_____

_____

_____

_____

_____

_____

_____

Biblical Thoughts and Themes

10.
Bible Verses

What verse in the Bible has had the greatest, long-lasting impact in your life?

Do you have it memorized?

Younger Question: Can you say any Bible verses by memory?

Which Bible verses do you like the most?

Psalm 119:9-11

How can a young man keep his way pure? By living according to your word. I seek you with all my heart; do not let me stray from your commands. I have hidden your word in my heart that I might not sin against you.

10.
Bible Verses

Personal Notes:

11.
Bible Books

Which book in the Bible do you most enjoy reading?

Why would you say it is your favorite?

Younger Question: What stories in the Bible do you like best?

Can you retell the story?

Joshua 1:8

Do not let this Book of the Law depart from your mouth; meditate on it day and night, so that you may be careful to do everything written in it. Then you will be prosperous and successful.

See also: Psalm 119

11.
Bible Books

Personal Notes:

_____

_____

_____

_____

_____

_____

_____

_____

_____

_____

_____

_____

_____

_____

_____

_____

_____

_____

Biblical Thoughts and Themes

12.
Talking to Jesus

If you lived in the days when Jesus walked the earth in human form, what questions would you have asked Him?

Younger Question: The Bible tells us that Jesus welcomed the little children to Himself and blessed them.

What would you have said to Jesus if you were one of those children?

Mark 10:13-16

People were bringing little children to Jesus to have him touch them, but the disciples rebuked them. When Jesus saw this, he was indignant. He said to them, "Let the little children come to me, and do not hinder them, for the kingdom of God belongs to such as these. I tell you the truth, anyone who will not receive the kingdom of God like a little child will never enter it." And he took the children in his arms, put his hands on them and blessed them.

12.
Talking to Jesus

Personal Notes:

_____

_____

_____

_____

_____

_____

_____

_____

_____

_____

_____

_____

_____

_____

_____

_____

_____

_____

_____

Trends, Fads and Inventions

fashions

trendsetters

inventors

ideas

Highlights of Human Interests

Trends, Fads and Inventions

ideas inventors

Trends, Fads, and Inventions
trendsetters
1.
Fashion Fads

Describe the craziest fashion fad that you actually wore.

Why did you wear it?

Younger Question: Can you name any funny or different fashion clothes that you have seen in the stores?

Why do you think people wear these items?

I Peter 3:3-4

Your beauty should not come from outward adornment, such as braided hair and the wearing of gold jewelry and fine clothes. Instead, it should be that of your inner self, the unfading beauty of a gentle and quiet spirit, which is of great worth in God's sight.

1.
Fashion Fads

Personal Notes:

_____

_____

_____

_____

_____

_____

_____

_____

_____

_____

_____

_____

_____

_____

_____

_____

_____

_____

_____

Your Invention

If cost, time, and materials were not an issue, what would you invent?

Describe its functions.

How would you market this invention?

Younger Question: If you could make a helpful machine or object which has never been made before, what would you make?

What would you call it?

II Chronicles 26:14-15

Uzziah provided shields, spears, helmets, coats of armor, bows and slingstones for the entire army. In Jerusalem he made machines designed by skillful men for use on the towers and on the corner defenses to shoot arrows and hurl large stones. His fame spread far and wide, for he was greatly helped until he became powerful.

2.
Your Invention

Personal Notes:

_____

_____

_____

_____

_____

_____

_____

_____

_____

_____

_____

_____

_____

_____

_____

_____

_____

_____

_____

3.
Trends

Name a trend (past or present) which you believe has been beneficial to our way of life.

Describe how or why.

Younger Question: A trend is a style or way of thinking that many people tend to follow (for instance colors they wear or music to which they listen).

Is it a good idea to follow what other people are doing?

Why?

I John 4:16

And so we know and rely on the love God has for us. God is love. Whoever lives in love lives in God, and God in him.

3.
Trends

Personal Notes: _____

_____

_____

_____

_____

_____

_____

_____

_____

_____

_____

_____

_____

_____

_____

_____

_____

_____

_____

4.
Starting Fads

How does a fad get started, and why do some fads make it big?

What fad would you start, if you had the influence to do so?

Younger Question: A fad is something that seems to be well liked by many people for a short period of time.

If you could get everybody to like something, what would it be?

Psalm 37:1-6

Do not fret because of evil men or be envious of those who do wrong; for like the grass they will soon wither, like green plants they will soon die away. Trust in the LORD and do good; dwell in the land and enjoy safe pasture. Delight yourself in the LORD and he will give you the desires of your heart. Commit your way to the LORD; trust in him and he will do this: He will make your righteousness shine like the dawn, the justice of your cause like the noonday sun.

4.
Starting Fads

Personal Notes:

5.
Trendsetters

Who would you say is the foremost trendsetter of the present time?

In what area of life are they setting a trend (fashion, music, politics, theology, etc.)?

Are they making a positive impact in our world?

Younger Question: Some people are leaders and some are followers. Of the friends that you know, who would you say are leaders.

Are they good people to follow?

Matthew 7:15-20

"Watch out for false prophets. They come to you in sheep's cloth-ing, but inwardly they are ferocious wolves. By their fruit you will recognize them. Do people pick grapes from thorn bushes, or figs from thistles? Likewise every good tree bears good fruit, but a bad tree bears bad fruit. A good tree cannot bear bad fruit, and a bad tree cannot bear good fruit. Every tree that does not bear good fruit is cut down and thrown into the fire. Thus, by their fruit you will recognize them.

5.
Trendsetters

Personal Notes:

_____

_____

_____

_____

_____

_____

_____

_____

_____

_____

_____

_____

_____

_____

_____

_____

_____

_____

Trends, Fads, and Inventions

6.
Inventors

Who would you say was the greatest inventor of all times?

Name some of his or her most significant inventions.

Younger Question: What do you think an inventor does?

Can you name one invention for which you are thankful?

Isaiah 64:8

Yet, O LORD, you are our Father. We are the clay, you are the potter; we are all the work of your hand.

6.
Inventors

Personal Notes:

7.
Diet Fads

What is the latest diet fad?

Is there evidence that it works?

Is it safe and nutritious?

In your opinion, has there ever been a diet fad that was successful?

Younger Question: What are some of your favorite foods?

Are some foods better for you to eat than others are?

Why is it important to eat healthy foods?

I Corinthians 6:19-20

Do you not know that your body is a temple of the Holy Spirit, who is in you, whom you have received from God? You are not your own; you were bought at a price. Therefore honor God with your body.

7.
Diet Fads

Personal Notes:

_____

_____

_____

_____

_____

_____

_____

_____

_____

_____

_____

_____

_____

_____

_____

_____

_____

_____

_____

8.
Current Fads

Describe some of the current fashion fads?

Are they a good idea for people to follow?

Why or why not?

Younger Question: If everybody you know started wearing goofy-looking, purple, furry hats, would you wear one too?

Why or why not?

How would you feel if you were the only one without a hat?

Matthew 6:28-34

"And why do you worry about clothes? See how the lilies of the field grow. They do not labor or spin. Yet I tell you that not even Solomon in all his splendor was dressed like one of these. If that is how God clothes the grass of the field, which is here today and tomorrow is thrown into the fire, will he not much more clothe you, O you of little faith? So do not worry, saying, 'What shall we eat?' or 'What shall we drink?' or 'What shall we wear?' For the pagans run after all these things, and your heavenly Father knows that you need them. But seek first his kingdom and his righteousness, and all these things will be given to you as well. Therefore do not worry about tomorrow, for tomorrow will worry about itself. Each day has enough trouble of its own.

8.
Current Fads

Personal Notes:

Trends, Fads, and Inventions
ideas, inventors, trendsetters
9.
Biblical Trends

Can you name several cultural trends that were prevalent in Jesus' time?

How did they effect the people of that time and their way of life?

Younger Question: In Jesus day, the Pharisees were the trendsetters. They made people follow many silly rules and ideas.

How do we know who to follow and what rules God wants us to obey?

II Timothy 3:16-17

All Scripture is God-breathed and is useful for teaching, rebuking, correcting and training in righteousness, so that the man of God may be thoroughly equipped for every good work.

See also: Romans 13

9.
Biblical Trends

Personal Notes:

_____

_____

_____

_____

_____

_____

_____

_____

_____

_____

_____

_____

_____

_____

_____

_____

_____

_____

_____

_____

_____

_____

10.
Wacky Inventions

What is the most peculiar or wacky invention you have ever heard of or seen?

What was the purpose of the invention?

Younger Question: Can you name a funny machine or invention you have heard about or seen?

Think about the books you read or videos you watch.

If you could make a wacky machine, what would it do?

Ecclesiastes 3:1-9

There is a time for everything, and a season for every activity under heaven: a time to be born and a time to die, a time to plant and a time to uproot, a time to kill and a time to heal, a time to tear down and a time to build, a time to weep and a time to laugh, a time to mourn and a time to dance, a time to scatter stones and a time to gather them, a time to embrace and a time to refrain, a time to search and a time to give up, a time to keep and a time to throw away, a time to tear and a time to mend, a time to be silent and a time to speak, a time to love and a time to hate, a time for war and a time for peace. What does the worker gain from his toil?

10.
Wacky Inventions

Personal Notes:

11.
Important Inventions

Of the following inventions, which one would you least want to part with? (light bulb, batteries, telephone, computer)

Why?

Younger Question: How would your life be different if you did not have light bulbs or batteries?

Have you ever thanked the Lord for some of the little things we use everyday?

Psalm 111:2-8

Great are the works of the LORD; they are pondered by all who delight in them. Glorious and majestic are his deeds, and his righteousness endures forever. He has caused his wonders to be remembered; the LORD is gracious and compassionate. He provides food for those who fear him; he remembers his covenant forever. He has shown his people the power of his works, giving them the lands of other nations. The works of his hands are faithful and just; all his precepts are trustworthy. They are steadfast for ever and ever, done in faithfulness and uprightness.

11.
Important Inventions

Personal Notes:

12.
Past Trends

If you could choose one decade or era from which to bring the fads, styles, and music into the present day, which time period would it be?

Why?

Younger Question: Have you seen pictures of your parents from when they were children?

What differences do you notice in clothing, hairstyles, and colors?

Is there anything you see in the pictures that you wish were around today? Why?

Philippians 3:12-13

Not that I have already obtained all this, or have already been made perfect, but I press on to take hold of that for which Christ Jesus took hold of me. Brothers, I do not consider myself yet to have taken hold of it. But one thing I do: Forgetting what is behind and straining toward what is ahead.

12.
Past Trends

Personal Notes:

_____

_____

_____

_____

_____

_____

_____

_____

_____

_____

_____

_____

_____

_____

_____

_____

_____